" "IT'S THE SHIP THAT MADE THE KESSEL RUN IN LESS THAN TWELVE PARSECS. I'VE OUTRUN IMPERIAL STARSHIPS. NOT THE LOCAL BULK CRUISERS, MIND YOU. I'M TALKING ABOUT THE BIG CORELLIAN SHIPS, NOW. SHE'S FAST ENOUGH FOR YOU, OLD MAN. **"**
– HAN SOLO

STAR WARS™

ANNUAL 2019

EGMONT
We bring stories to life

First published in Great Britain 2018 by Egmont UK Limited
The Yellow Building, 1 Nicholas Road, London W11 4AN

Written by Ned Hartley
Designed by Alex Fanning
Cover design by Richie Hull

© & ™ 2018 Lucasfilm Ltd.
ISBN 978 1 4052 9113 2
68213/001
Printed in Italy

To find more great *Star Wars* books, visit www.egmont.co.uk/starwars

Stay safe online. Any website addresses listed in this book are correct at the time of going to print. However, Egmont is not responsible for content hosted by third parties. Please be aware that online content can be subject to change and websites can contain content that is unsuitable for children. We advise that all children are supervised when using the internet.

Egmont takes its responsibility to the planet and its inhabitants very seriously. All the papers we use are from well-managed forests run by responsible suppliers.

Welcome to the *Star Wars* Annual 2019!

Inside you'll find lots of facts and features about *Star Wars: The Last Jedi* and *Solo: A Star Wars Story*, as well as much, much more from a galaxy far, far away!

Please do watch out for the porgs, though. They managed to get in and now they're everywhere. See if you can spot seven hiding among the pages.

Write your name, species and homeworld below, and let's begin!

NAME:

SPECIES:

HOMEWORLD:

CONTENTS

FACT FILE: THE RESISTANCE

WHO ARE THE RESISTANCE?

After the First Order destroyed the peaceful New Republic, the Resistance is the last, best hope for freedom in the galaxy.

▲ POE DAMERON

He's a hot-headed pilot who thinks any problem can be solved by jumping into an X-wing and blowing things up! Poe is the best pilot in the fleet, but he's also one of the worst at taking orders.

▲ FINN

A former stormtrooper called FN-2187, Finn escaped the First Order and bravely helped the Resistance. He is beginning to learn that sometimes you need to have something worth fighting for...

▲ VICE-ADMIRAL HOLDO

One of Leia Organa's oldest friends, Amilyn Holdo moves quickly and doesn't like discussing her plans with others. She thinks that Poe Dameron's schemes are foolhardy and dangerous.

▲ BB-8

This tiny astromech droid has saved the day more than once! BB-8 normally fits in Poe Dameron's X-wing to help him fly, but he's also full of useful surprises!

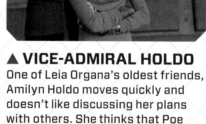

▲ GENERAL LEIA ORGANA

The sister of Luke Skywalker and daughter of Darth Vader. General Leia set up the Resistance when she saw that the New Republic was not doing enough to counter the growing threat of the First Order.

"WE ARE THE SPARK THAT WILL LIGHT THE FIRE THAT WILL BURN THE FIRST ORDER DOWN!"
Poe Dameron

[X-WING]

[A-WING]

[BOMBER]

[SKI SPEEDER]

▲ REY

Rey is a scavenger from Jakku, who desperately wants to know who her family is. When she meets Finn and the Resistance she starts to see a place for herself, and will do whatever it takes to help out.

▲ ROSE TICO

Rose is a maintenance technician who helps keep the Resistance fleet running. She tells Finn that *"We're going to win this war not by fighting what we hate, but by saving what we love!*

▲ LUKE SKYWALKER

This legendary Jedi helped destroy the Death Star, defeat Emperor Palpatine and bring down the Galactic Empire. But after his Jedi Academy failed he fled to hide away on the remote planet Ahch-To.

FACT FILE: THE FIRST ORDER

WHO ARE THE FIRST ORDER?

A powerful military faction which rose from the ruins of the Galactic Empire. Using the terrifying Starkiller Base, they crushed the New Republic and now reign supreme.

◀ GENERAL HUX

Armitage Hux is ambitious, ruthless and cruel! He fought against the New Republic because he thought it was weak and decadent, and now he wants to smash the Resistance. Hux is in competition for power with Kylo Ren, even though they are both on the same side.

"ALL REMAINING SYSTEMS WILL BOW TO THE FIRST ORDER!"
General Hux

▲ PRAETORIAN GUARD

Supreme Leader Snoke is always surrounded by highly-trained warriors. Their powered weapons allow them to fight opponents with lightsabers. The Praetorian Guard are the fiercest, strongest warriors in the First Order.

▲ CAPTAIN PHASMA

The stormtrooper captain has a suit made from polished chrome that can deflect standard blaster bolts. She managed to escape the destruction of Starkiller Base, and controls a squadron of deadly stormtroopers.

[ASHES OF THE EMPIRE]

The First Order contains officers, soldiers and scientists who were part of Emperor Palpatine's evil Galactic Empire. After Palpatine died the Empire was taken apart by the New Republic, but many Imperial forces fled to the Unknown Regions of the galaxy where they built the First Order.

▲ SUPREME LEADER SNOKE

This mysterious leader commands the First Order and has an incredibly powerful connection to the dark side of the Force. Snoke wants complete control of the galaxy and needs to wipe out anyone who stands in his way. He is a cruel and unforgiving leader, and he loves tormenting his student, Kylo Ren!

◄ KYLO REN

The son of Han Solo and Leia Organa, Kylo Ren first trained with Luke Skywalker. Luke could see the growing darkness in him, but was not able to stop Kylo Ren destroying his Jedi academy. Kylo Ren is strong in the Force, but is conflicted about what he should do with his power. He killed his father, Han Solo, but still feels the pull of the light side of the Force.

"LET THE PAST DIE. KILL IT IF YOU HAVE TO. THAT'S THE ONLY WAY TO BECOME WHAT YOU WERE MEANT TO BE."

Kylo Ren

PRAETORIAN WEAPONS

▲

[VIBRO-VOULGE]

▲

[BILARI ELECTRO-CHAIN WHIP]

▲

[TWIN VIBRO-ARBIR BLADES]

THE FIRST ORDER ATTACKS!

The First Order are attacking the Resistance!
Can you help the Resistance survive to fight another day?

SENSOR SCANS!
The Resistance has been scanning the First Order fleet! Work out which
Star Destroyer is targeting the Resistance by matching the right shadow.

REWIRE POE'S X-WING!
BB-8 needs help fixing the circuits on the weapon systems
on Poe Dameron's X-wing! Connect the points of the same
colour with each other, but make sure they don't cross!

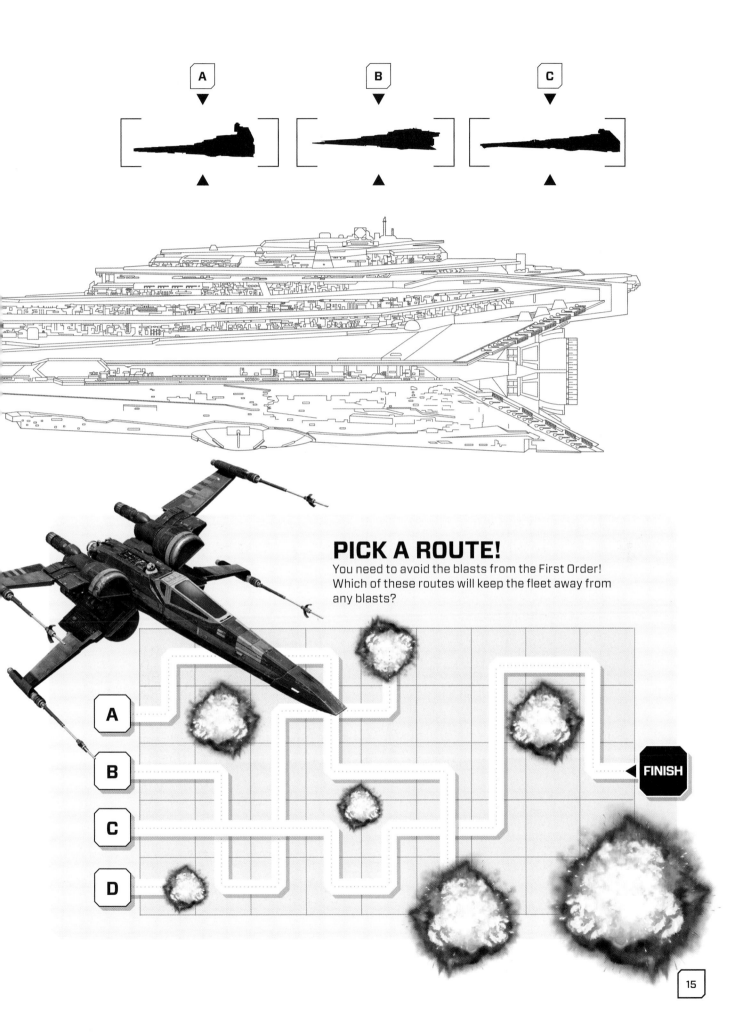

PICK A ROUTE!

You need to avoid the blasts from the First Order!
Which of these routes will keep the fleet away from
any blasts?

FINISH

KYLO REN'S TIE SILENCER

Kylo Ren has a new prototype starfighter designed to take on the Resistance fleet! Everything about the TIE silencer is faster, stronger and more deadly than a normal TIE fighter!

SOLAR ARRAY

[FACT FILE]
Name: TIE silencer
Affiliation: First Order
Manufacturer: Sienar-Jaemus Fleet Systems
Length: 57.19ft
Width: 25ft
Height: 12.34ft
Weapons: Twin laser cannons, twin heavy laser cannons, proton torpedo launchers

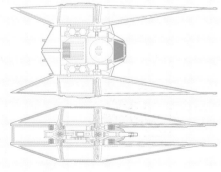

MAIN TRANSPARISTEEL VEIWPORT

POWER GENERATOR

PROTON TORPEDO LAUNCHER

LASER CANNONS

KYLO REN – PILOT

Kylo Ren's force-enhanced reflexes mean that he is an exceptionally fast and skillful pilot.

He is not completely consumed by the dark side. At the height of battle Kylo Ren is unable to fire the blast that will destroy his mother, Leia Organa.

Kylo still manages to do heavy damage to the Resistance fleet, blowing up a hangar full of ships.

HOW TO DRAW PORGS

The planet Ahch-To, where Luke Skywalker now lives, is home to these big-eyed, feathered creatures. Learn how to draw porgs by copying this one into the grid opposite!

CANTO BIGHT PUZZLES

Finn and **Rose** need some luck! Help them win in the casino at Canto Bight!

CASH YOUR CHIPS!

Every one of these chips has a pair apart from one – Which is it?

SECURITY CAMERAS

The security footage in the casino is being scrambled!
Can you work out which three pictures are of **Rose**, **Finn** and **BB-8**?

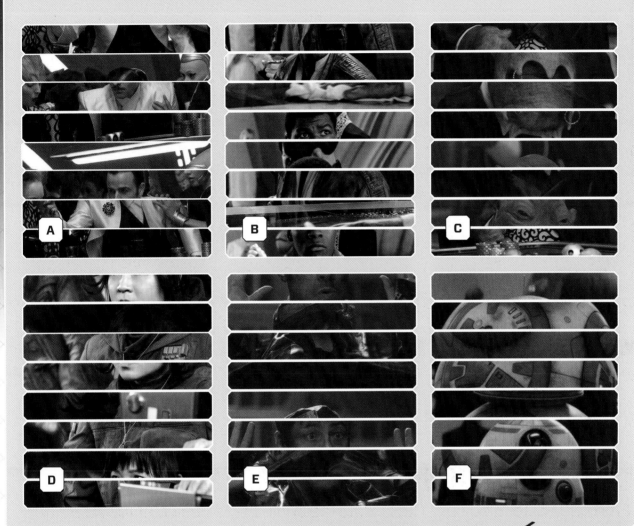

A B C

D E F

AVOID THE POLICE!

Which of these three routes will take you
to Finn instead of the Canto Bight police?

A

B

C

[FACT FILE]
These massive walkers carry turbolaser cannons to blast the enemies of the First Order! They have extra joints in their front feet to give extra stability.

SPOT THE DIFFERENCE
Can you spot SIX differences between these huge AT-M6 walkers?

DROID COLOURING

THE SECRET TUNNELS OF CRAIT

While the battle rages overhead, the brave Resistance need to escape the First Order! Find a route to help them through the tunnels and escape to the *Millennium Falcon!*

[HINT]
Follow the Vulptexes if you get lost!

START

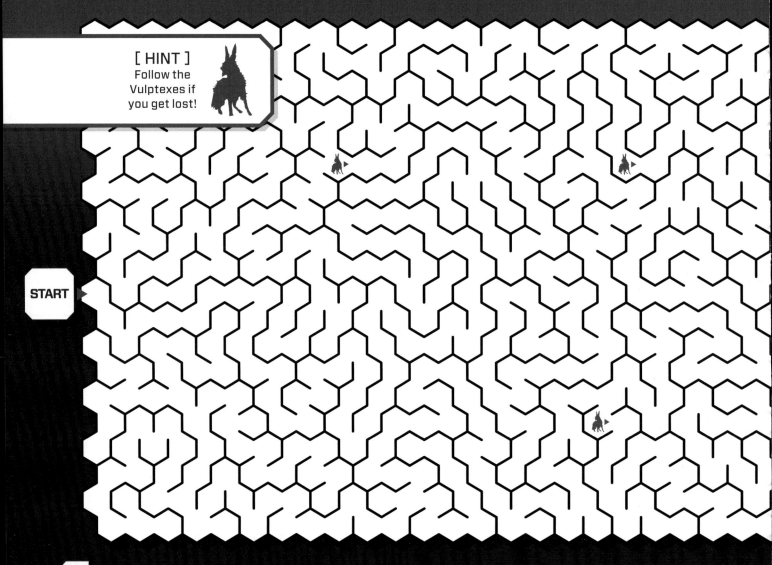

FINISH

THE HISTORY OF THE JEDI

Everything you need to know about these incredible warriors.

LIGHTSABERS
Jedi normally chose to use a lightsaber in battle, a weapon which was made up of a glowing plasma blade coming from a metal hilt. Lightsabers were incredibly powerful, they could chop down enemies, deflect blaster fire and even cut through metal doors!

WHAT IS THE FORCE?
The Force is an energy that binds the universe together. Jedi used the Force to give themselves amazing powers. They could jump higher, run faster and move quicker than anyone, plus the Force allowed them to move things using only their minds!

JEDI ROBES
Jedi tended to wear long, flowing robes with a utility belt to hook their lightsaber. The utility belt usually held lots of other useful things like a grappling hook, an underwater breather, a lightsaber repair kit and a communication device.

THE JEDI TEMPLE

The planet Coruscant was the home of the Jedi Order for thousands of years. The Jedi Temple was a place for Jedi to train, learn and organise. The Jedi Archives stored information from all over the galaxy and was fiercely guarded by the Jedi.

ORDER 66 AND THE FALL OF THE JEDI

Emperor Palpatine used the Clone Wars to gain power, and no-one suspected he was secretly the Sith Lord called Darth Sidious. Palpatine issued Order 66, commanding his clone troopers to attack the Jedi. Only a few survived.

JEDHA

Jedha was home to one of the first civilisations to use the Force. It was the source of many kyber crystals that could be used to make lightsabers. It was later taken over by the Galactic Empire, who used the kyber crystals to power the Death Star.

FACT FILE: THE JEDI

▲ **ANAKIN SKYWALKER**
Many Jedi believed that Anakin Skywalker was the Chosen One, who would bring balance to the Force. Anakin ended up turned to the dark side of the Force and becoming Darth Vader, killing hundreds of Jedi. He died saving his son, Luke, from Darth Sidious.

▲ **MACE WINDU**
An imposing Jedi Master who was known for his purple-bladed lightsaber and his no-nonsense attitude. He was a formidable fighter and even beat the deadly bounty hunter Jango Fett in the arena at Geonosis. He was killed by Darth Sidious' Force lightning.

▲ **MASTER YODA**
Although small, Jedi Master Yoda had such a strong connection to the Force that he was extremely powerful. Yoda trained Jedi for over 800 years, but had to flee when Darth Sidious destroyed the Jedi. Yoda hid on the swamp planet Dagobah for years, and later trained the young Luke Skywalker.

OBI-WAN KENOBI
Obi-Wan was Anakin Skywalker's Jedi Master and when Anakin turned to the dark side Obi-Wan went into hiding. He took the name "Ben Kenobi" and stayed on the planet Tatooine, watching over Anakin's son Luke as he grew up.

▲ **LUKE SKYWALKER**
The son of Darth Vader, Luke became a powerful Jedi like his father. Luke was hugely important in the destruction of the first Death Star and the fall of the Empire, and after Palpatine died Luke tried to set up a new order of Jedi to return peace to the galaxy.

▼ REY

Feeling an affinity with Anakin and Luke's old lightsaber, Rey sought out Luke Skywalker and trained with him on the planet Ahch-to. She is incredibly strong in the Force, and was able to use Jedi abilities without any formal training.

KYLO REN

Ben Solo decided to follow in the footsteps of his grandfather Darth Vader. He took the name Kylo Ren and destroyed Luke's new Jedi Order, killing the other Jedi and becoming part of the deadly Knights of Ren.

[THE NEW JEDI ORDER]

Luke Skywalker took a new generation of Jedi and taught them everything he knew about the Force. One of the Jedi was Han Solo and Leia Organa's son Ben Solo, who was a strong but conflicted young man. Luke knew that Ben was powerful in the Force, but he thought that he could control him.

DARTH VADER PUZZLES

WORDSEARCH

How many words related to **Darth Vader** can you find in this wordsearch?
They can be found going up, down, backwards, forwards and diagonally.

```
E X R N J D U T D E Q Y N J H
P D V E C V R C A M W G K T F
L J Q V B A X Q L D E X A K U
F Q Y K N A Y L E A V E K A I
H T R A D M S N U P D J E D I
M Y K H N Y I T E K D U S S F
D I M Z W T G K H S E T M H Y
N I C F A A R M R G A T I G Q
E W N P J T V Q E R I E D F D
C O L Q B X K L K R T L W U B
F A Z H Y H S Q L W E D P U E
P E M P E R O R A W M D B T I
W O X S J I F U W B M A A T W
P C D Y Z X F N Y Q A Y H V A
R I F R I J F V K Z B A U C R
C F X A A W Q L S Q F N G C R
A O A N T C Q E B R V B Y T I
K Z M O B F E I N Q V F Z A O
L F O Y Z S A A B M D H O Z R
X Q Z U M V V E Y A U V P N B
```

WORDS TO FIND:

- DARTH
- VADER
- ANAKIN
- SKYWALKER
- LIGHTSABER
- EMPEROR
- PALPATINE
- JEDI
- LUKE
- LEIA
- PODRACE
- WARRIOR
- DEATH
- STAR

HIDDEN TARGETS!

Vader is trying to use the Force, but something is clouding his vision . . .
Can you work out who these characters are?

A

B

C

D

ODD STORMTROOPER OUT!

Lord Vader is inspecting the troops, but one of these stormtroopers is NOT wearing the correct uniform!
Find out which of these stormtroopers is different from the others so that he can be disciplined!

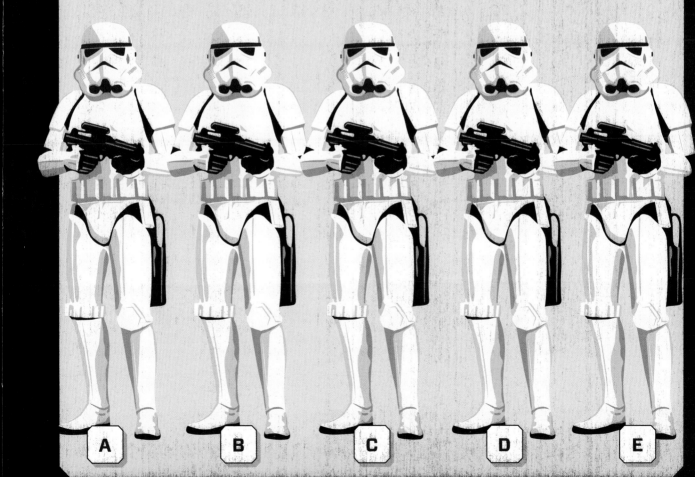

Darth Vader has his very own specially-modified TIE Advanced with cluster missile launchers, a shield generator and a hyperdrive. Even with all the extra gear it's still as fast as a normal TIE fighter.

THE FASTEST SHIPS IN THE GALAXY!

See how the the different starships in the galaxy match up in the speed department.

The special forces First Order TIE fighter has a seat at the front for the pilot and a seat at the back for a gunner.

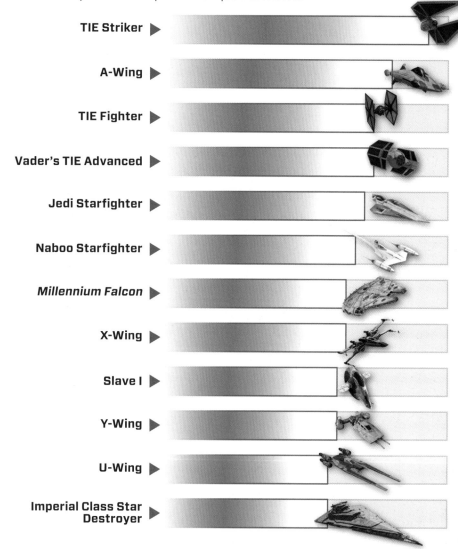

- TIE Striker ▶
- A-Wing ▶
- TIE Fighter ▶
- Vader's TIE Advanced ▶
- Jedi Starfighter ▶
- Naboo Starfighter ▶
- *Millennium Falcon* ▶
- X-Wing ▶
- Slave I ▶
- Y-Wing ▶
- U-Wing ▶
- Imperial Class Star Destroyer ▶

Ships travel vast distances through a dimension called hyperspace. The route has to be precisely plotted, and if the hyperdrive is damaged or broken a ship cannot jump.

LIGHTSABER REPAIR

These lightsabers have been cut into pieces during a Jedi battle!
Can you work out which pieces fit together to fix the lightsabers?
Remember – the Jedi are counting on you!

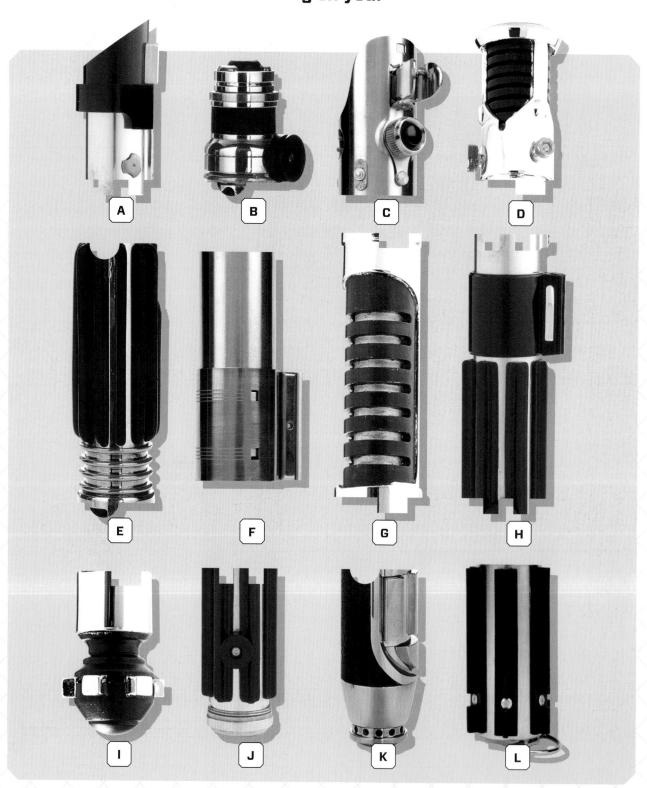

FORCE PUZZLES

If you want to be a Jedi then you'll need to work hard. Is the Force strong enough in you to find the answers below?

SCRAMBLED NAMES

Use the Force to unscramble the names of these Jedi heroes!

1. UNWE DMICA

2. WEA KON IONBIB

3. SULK YWALKREEK

4. DAYO

FORCE SHADOWS

Only the silhouettes of these figures are visible. Can you use the Force to work out who they are?

A

B

C

D

HOW TO WIN A PODRACE

Podracing is one of the fastest and most dangerous sports in the galaxy! Do you have what it takes to win?

MAKE YOUR PODRACER

If you want to race then you're going to need a podracer! Podracers are made up of a pod for the driver to sit in, which is attached to engines that make it go really fast!

CHOOSE YOUR ENGINE

DESIGN YOUR FLAG!

Your fans in the crowd are going to need something to wave! Draw a cool and eye-catching design on this blank flag.

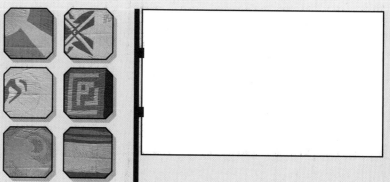

Anakin Skywalker was a great podracer when he was young. He was the only human who could handle the incredible speeds involved!

▶ **USE THE FORCE**
Podracers travel much faster than normal humans can handle, so you'll need to be strong in the Force to race these things!

▶ **DON'T BE A CHEATER!**
Sebulba tried to sabotage Anakin's podracer. It nearly helped him win, but he was ultimately defeated!

▶ **GET THE RIGHT GEAR**
You're definitely going to need goggles to stop tiny bugs flying in your eyes!

DRAW YOUR PODRACER!

FACT FILE: R2-D2

This awesome astromech is one of the coolest droids ever created! He's brave, loyal and can be trusted with anything!

X-WING

R2-D2 is an astromech droid, which means he slots neatly into an X-wing and helps fly the starfighter.

[FACT FILE]
Model: R2 series astromech droid
Weapons: Electroshock prod, buzzsaw
Other Features: Holographic projector, data port
Height: 3' 7"
Affiliation: Galactic Republic, Rebel Alliance, the Resistance

▲

He's full of hidden compartments and surprises! You don't want to get zapped by his electroshock prod!

▲

R2's best friend is C-3PO, and even though the two are constantly arguing they have shared many exciting adventures together.

▲

He can be upgraded with cool add-ons like rocket boosters to make him fly! When he was on Jabba's sail barge he only had a drinks tray, which wasn't quite so cool.

DESTROY THE DEATH STAR!

The Rebel Alliance needs your help! Brave Jyn Erso and her crew have stolen the plans to the Death Star from the Empire – help us make sense of them so that our fighters can take it down!

MISSING PIECE

The plans to the Death Star have become corrupted in the transfer.
Which of these is the missing piece of the schematics?

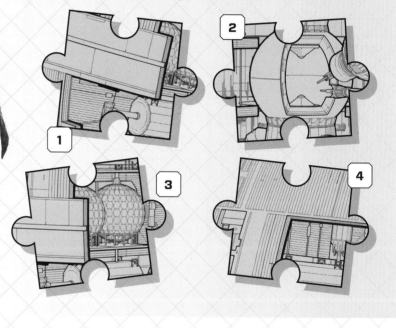

WHICH EXHAUST PORT?

We know that to destroy the Death Star we need to fire a proton torpedo into a thermal exhaust port, and it will travel directly into the reactor.
Which exhaust port should we target?

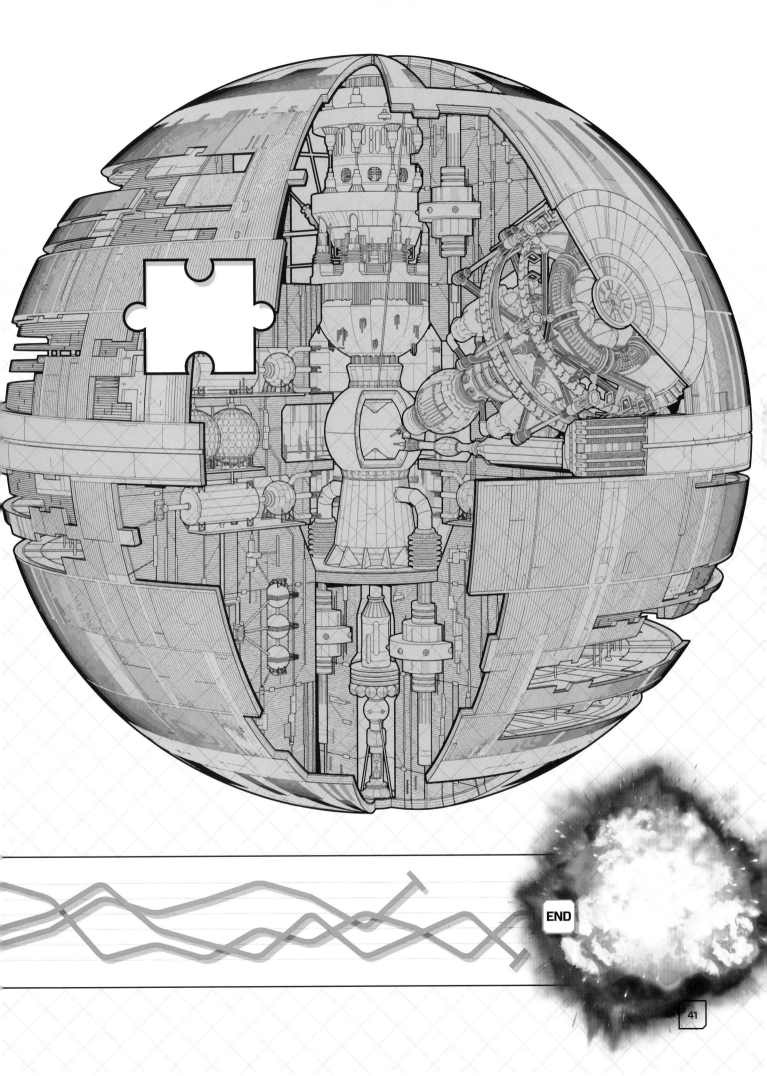

WEAPONS TRAINING

Arm yourself with knowledge about the deadliest weapons around!

MAGNAGUARD

STORMTROOPER

BOBA FETT

EXECUTIONER TROOPER

ELECTROSTAFF

These long, crackling melee weapons were used by General Grievous' Magnaguard droids during the Clone Wars. They were able to defend their master against Jedi, because their electrified ends can deflect lightsabers.

BLASTER

Blasters come in lots of different shapes and sizes, but they all fire bolts of explosive energy. A Jedi's lightsaber can be used to defend from blaster fire, and a really good Jedi can deflect the bolt back at the blaster that fired it!

HIDDEN WEAPONRY

Like the bounty hunter himself, Boba Fett's armour is full of surprises, including rocket dart launchers in his kneepads! Built into his gauntlets are a flamethrower, a laser and concussion missile launcher.

LASER AXE

When the cruel First Order executes an enemy spy or traitor, they want it to hurt. These special Executioner Troopers, in their distinctive black and white armour, use scary and painful laser axes to deliver their 'justice'.

RIOT CONTROL TROOPER

CHEWBACCA

REY

CHIRRUT ÎMWE

RIOT CONTROL BATON
Finn was trained in the use of this First Order weapon, which doesn't kill, but really hurts! It can spin around to knock down enemies, and as it is electrified means that it's a good weapon to use against a lightsaber.

BOWCASTER
Chewbacca uses this traditional Wookiee weapon, a sort of plasma crossbow. It's more powerful than a standard blaster and much heavier. Han Solo sometimes borrowed it from Chewie, saying "I like this thing!"

REY'S STAFF
Rey needed something strong and sturdy to keep her safe on Jakku. She trained hard and became extremely skilled with her staff. She could knock down a whole team of Unkar Plutt's men without even breaking a sweat!

LIGHTBOW
Chirrut Îmwe carries a lightbow, the weapon used traditionally by the Guardians of the Whills. Chirrut hand-crafted his lightbow himself. It's so powerful that he could use it to shoot down a TIE fighter with only one hit!

THE TOUGHEST BAD GUYS

▲ KYLO REN
Darth Vader's grandson embraced the dark side and wanted to be just like his grandfather. He was powerful, but be careful – he lashed out when he was angry!

▲ EMPEROR PALPATINE
He could fry you where you stood with his Force lightning. He was Darth Vader's Sith Master and taught him about the dark side of the Force!

▲ BOBA FETT
The greatest bounty hunter that ever lived could track a target from one side of the galaxy to the other! He had a jetpack and a suit of armour that was packed with deadly hidden weapons!

DARTH MAUL
A Sith so strong that he could fight two Jedi at the same time with his double-bladed lightsaber, Darth Maul was even able to survive being cut in half by Obi-Wan Kenobi. Maul returned with a set of robot legs, ready for revenge!

▲ CAPTAIN PHASMA
She ruled her squadron of stormtroopers with an iron (well, chrome-covered) fist. Phasma commanded the respect of her men, apart from Finn who shoved her in a trash compactor.

DARTH VADER

Once a Jedi, then the scariest man in the galaxy, the Force was so strong with Darth Vader that he didn't even need to be on the same spaceship as someone to use his powers on them! There was almost nobody in the galaxy that could beat him.

▲ GENERAL GRIEVOUS

Grievous loved nothing more than destroying Jedi, and he carried the lightsabers of those he had defeated in combat. He was rebuilt with a cyborg body after a terrible accident almost killed him.

COUNT DOOKU

Also known as the Sith Lord Darth Tyranus, he was part of Palpatine's plans to use the Clone Wars to end the age of the Jedi. However, he wasn't around to see his plans come to fruition, because Anakin Skywalker cut his head off.

WHERE'S THE WOOKIEE?

Chewbacca is on Scarif, where a fierce battle is raging between the Rebel Alliance and the Empire! Can you find him in this busy scene?

When you have found Chewbacca, see if you can spot Gungi and Ulibacca!

See many more Wookiee hunts in the amazing *Where's the Wookiee?* activity books!

FACT FILE: THE UNDERWORLD

HAN SOLO
Affiliation: None

Han grew up on the planet of Corellia and was forced to turn to petty criminal activities to survive. He's smart, scrappy and he knows how to take a punch.

CHEWBACCA
Affiliation: None

Chewie is a brave and loyal Wookiee from the planet Kashyyyk. His huge size means that he can be pretty scary, but he's actually quite sweet once you get to know him.

LANDO CALRISSIAN
Affiliation: None

Smooth and sophisticated, Lando is ready to retire from his life as a smuggler. He owns the *Millennium Falcon* and keeps it in tip-top condition.

L3-37
Affiliation: None

Lando's co-pilot is a self-made droid who cares deeply about droids' rights. She is an expert navigator whose droid brain keeps the *Falcon* on course and out of danger.

Don't trust any of these rogues and scoundrels!

ENFYS NEST
Affiliation:
Cloud Riders

The mysterious and deadly leader of the Cloud Riders, who strike from nowhere, often taking the spoils of other criminals. Well-trained in martial arts and a crack shot.

QI'RA
Affiliation:
Crimson Dawn

Han's friend Qi'ra grew up with him on Corellia. She is very smart and knows that sometimes you have to make difficult decisions to get what you want in life.

MOLOCH
Affiliation:
The White Worms

The fearsome enforcer for the White Worms gang, he is devious and underhanded. He is extremely sensitive to light, and cannot stand to be in direct sunlight.

MUDTROOPER
Affiliation:
Galactic Empire

These specialised stormtroopers are fighting rebels on the planet of Mimban. Their armour has been adapted to function in the wet, muddy environment on Mimban.

HOW TO BE LIKE HAN SOLO!

Follow our tips to copy the style of the supercool smuggler!
This guide will make you totally Han-tastic!

1 Be cool
Han Solo never loses his cool, even when faced with nearly impossible odds! Practise your confident swagger and always be ready with a snappy comeback!

2 Take risks
Han is always looking for the big payoff, and that can mean doing things that you've never done before. Sometimes you have to do new and exciting things, and it can be really rewarding!

3 Get up when life knocks you down
Not everything in life is always going to go your way. When things go wrong for Han he doesn't give up or sulk. He gets up, dusts himself off and tries again!

4 Learn another language
You don't have to learn how to speak Wookiee, but it always helps to speak as many languages as possible if you want to make good deals – and good friends.

5 Look out for your friends
Han will always try to help his friends if he can, he has learned the hard way that abandoning your friends will only lead to heartache!

6 Be clever
Sometimes you have to be a little bit... creative in order to get what you want. That's not to say you should break the law like Han does you're not fighting the Empire, after all, but a little bit of cleverness will always help you come out on top.

Just trust me!

I got this!

[SOUND LIKE HAN!]
Practise saying these phrases just like Han!

I can do this!

[GET THE LOOK!]
A rugged but stylish jacket, sturdy boots, a collarless shirt and simple black vest!

DRAW A CO-PILOT!
Han has Chewie, but you're going to need a friend to help you out when you get in trouble! Draw your buddy here:
Do they have?
[ ] Furry arms
[ ] Robot legs
[ ] Eyes on stalks

THE *MILLENNIUM FALCON*

Take a tour around the brand-new *Falcon*!

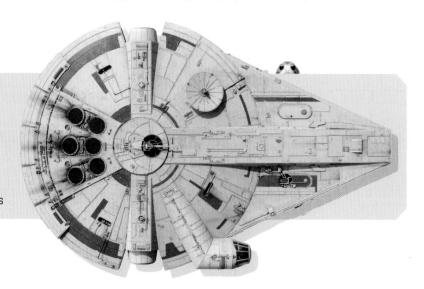

[FACT FILE]
Name: The *Millennium Falcon*
Affiliation: None
Manufacturer: Corellian
Engineering Corporation
Type: YT-1300 light freighter
Length: 113.25ft
Weapons: Quad laser cannons

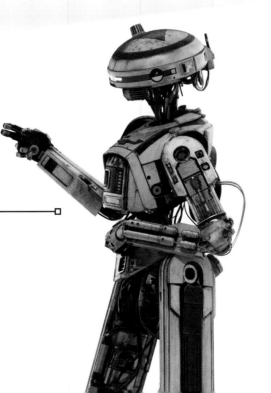

L3-37

Lando's co-pilot on the *Falcon* is L3-37. L3 is a droid and can fly faster than any human pilot!

FAMOUS FREIGHTER

▲

The *Falcon* was originally owned by Lando Calrissian. He made sure it was always well-stocked and was one of the most comfortable ships around!

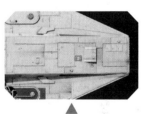

▲

The escape pod comes out from the front of the ship! Careful you don't lose it, because those things are really hard to replace...

▲

The *Falcon* is a great ship for smugglers because it is full of compartments for hiding contraband. Even when Imperial search parties board the ship they can't find everything.

PLAY SABACC!
This high-stakes card game is a favourite of Lando and Han!

RULES
■ Add up all the numbers on the cards in each hand.
■ The winner is the person who has either 23 or -23
■ There's a special hand called an "Idiot's Array", which is a 0, 2 and 3. If you have those three cards you beat everyone else.

HAN'S HAND

Han is holding the top two cards. Which of the cards below does he need to win?

Han, Qi'ra, Lando and Chewbacca have the following cards. Which of them has the winning hand?

THE WINNER: ☐ A. QI'RA   ☐ B. CHEWBACCA   ☐ C. HAN SOLO   ☐ D. LANDO

FALCON PUZZLES!

Han, Lando and Chewie want to take off, but something is wrong! Fix the ship and help them on their way!

STRIPS OF A SHIP!
Put these parts of the *Falcon* in the right order!

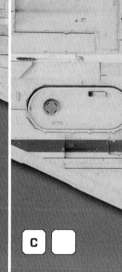

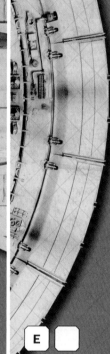

 A
 B
 C
 D
 E

IGNITION SEQUENCE
Help Chewie start the ship by working out what comes next in this sequence.

1 ▸ ▸ ▸ ▸ [?]

F

G | | H | | I | | J | |

FIX THE SHIP!
Which of these pieces is NOT from the *Falcon*?

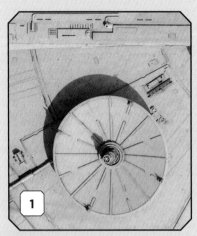

1

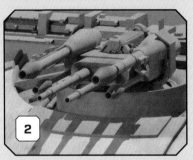

2

3

4

[HINT]
Have a look at the blueprints on page 54 if you need to jog your memory.

SCOUNDREL COLOURING

SMUGGLERS' CODE

To avoid Imperial attention these criminals have been sending messages in code.

CAN YOU CRACK THE CODE AND WORK OUT WHAT THEY ARE SAYING?

A	B	C	D	E	F	G	H	I	J	K	L	M	N	O	P	Q	R	S	T	U	V	W	X	Y	Z

HAN, LANDO OR CHEWIE?

Follow this simple quiz to find out which of these *Star Wars* characters you are most like!

1. IF SOMEONE IS BEING MEAN TO YOU, DO YOU NORMALLY TRY TO...

[A] Steal something from them when they aren't looking.
[B] Charm them! I can be very persuasive!
[C] Yell at them! RAAAARRRRGHH!

2. WHICH OF THESE IS MOST IMPORTANT IN A SPACE SHIP?

[A] I want it to zoom as fast as possible.
[B] It should look really, really good!
[C] I like to tinker and make modifications.

3. WOULD YOU EVER CHEAT AT A CARD GAME?

[A] Not if I thought I would get caught.
[B] Maybe. Ok, all the time.
[C] NO! That makes me ANGRY!

4. DESCRIBE YOUR BEST FRIEND.

[A] Bigger and stronger than me.
[B] I have lots of friends, but I don't have a best friend
[C] Smaller and better at talking than me.

5. WOULD YOU EVER GET IN A FIGHT TO PROTECT A FRIEND?

[A] Yes, but I'd try to think my way round it first.
[B] Absolutely not. My clothes might get dirty.
[C] Oh yeah! Bring it ON!

6. WOULD YOU EVER DO A DEAL WITH SOMEONE YOU THOUGHT WASN'T VERY NICE?

[A] Depends on the deal.
[B] Sure, I'm open to anything.
[C] I don't think so.

7. WHAT IS THE BEST WAY TO GET OUT OF TROUBLE?

[A] Think my way out.
[B] Talk my way out.
[C] Fight my way out.

8. WHAT IS THE MOST IMPORTANT PART OF A SPACE SHIP?

[A] The engines.
[B] The drinks bar.
[C] The weapons.

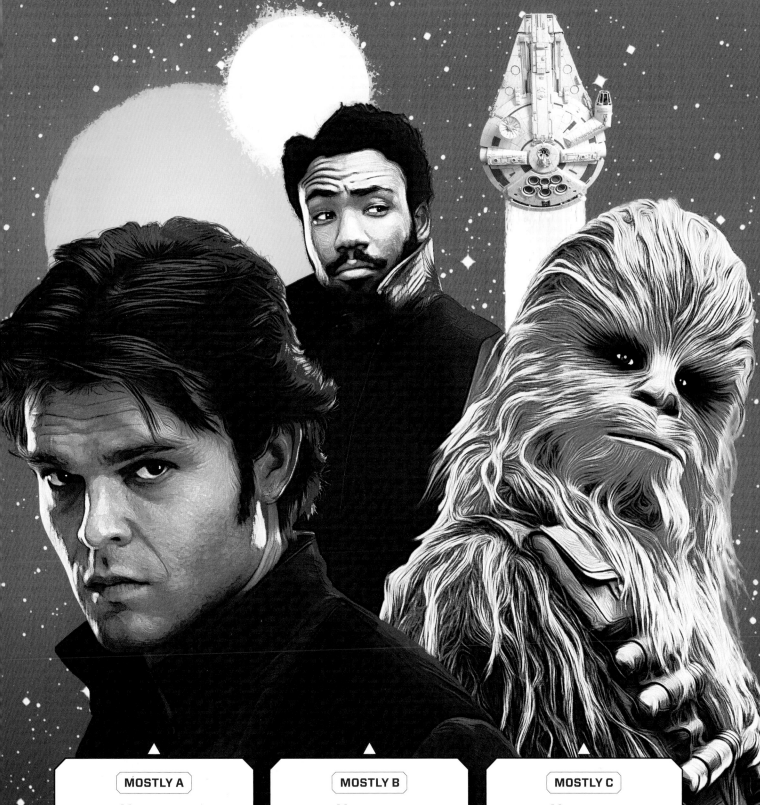

MOSTLY A

You are...
HAN SOLO!
You're brash and cocky, but you're also pretty smart! You believe in yourself, and you TRY to do the right thing, even if sometimes things can be a little complicated.

MOSTLY B

You are...
LANDO CALRISSIAN!
You're a smooth scoundrel who always knows the right thing to say! Even though you aren't always honest, you are always great company and good fun to be around!

MOSTLY C

You are...
CHEWBACCA!
You're very strong and tough, but you also have a sensitive side! You are extremely loyal to your friends and would do anything to help them!

THE KESSEL RUN

Can you complete this dangerous route for smugglers without destroying the *Falcon*?

START

NO

Use your emergency supply of coaxium?

YES

A plasma storm is drawing in! Do you fly through it?

NO

YES

NO

Your ship is too heavy. Dump the cargo?

YES

YES

TIE fighters are chasing you! Do you try to fight them?

NO

YES

NO

Two carbonbergs are in the way! Squeeze between them?

YES

You've nearly made it! Sneak in to Kessel?

NO

FINISH

NO

The gravity on the ship starts to change! Do you change course?

YES

Well done! You completed the Kessel Run! You are now at the spice mines of Kessel!

MASTER OF THE FORCE: QUIZ

HOW WELL DO YOU KNOW THE WORLD OF STAR WARS?

Answer these questions to show your stuff!

01 WHO WAS DARTH VADER'S MASTER?
[A] Emperor Palpatine
[B] Jar-Jar Binks
[C] Senator Bail Organa

02 WHAT IS THE NAME OF THE CRYSTAL THAT POWERS A LIGHTSABER?

03 WHICH SITH HAD A DOUBLE-BLADED LIGHTSABER?

04 WHO HAD THE *MILLENNIUM FALCON* BEFORE HAN SOLO?
[A] Darth Vader
[B] Lando Calrissian
[C] Luke Skywalker

05 WHAT IS BOBA FETT'S FAMOUS PROFESSION?

06 WHAT SPORT DID YOUNG ANAKIN SKYWALKER COMPETE IN?

07 WHO IS HAN SOLO'S SON?

08 WHO IS LUKE SKYWALKER'S FATHER?

09 WHO GUARDS SUPREME LEADER SNOKE?

10 WHAT PLANET DID YODA HIDE ON AFTER THE FALL OF THE JEDI?

11 WHAT IS THE NAME OF THE FIRST ORDER SUPERWEAPON THAT WAS DESTROYED BY THE RESISTANCE?

12 WHAT IS THE NAME OF THE FIRST ORDER GENERAL?

13 WHICH OF THESE IS NOT A REBEL SHIP?
[A] X-wing [B] A-wing
[C] W-wing

14 WHAT TYPE OF AN ALIEN IS CHEWBACCA?

15 WHAT COLOUR IS MACE WINDU'S LIGHTSABER?

16 WHAT NAME DOES OBI-WAN KENOBI USE WHEN HE'S HIDING ON TATOOINE?

17 WHAT PLANET DOES REY FIND LUKE LIVING ON?

18 WHAT TYPE OF DROID IS BB-8?

19 WHAT WAS FINN'S NAME WHEN HE WAS A STORMTROOPER?

20 WHAT PLANET DID REY GROW UP ON?

ANSWERS

14-15 Sensor Scans: B
Rewire Poe's W-Wing:

Pick a Route: C

20-21 Cash Your Chips: 8
Security Cameras:
Rose - D
Finn - B
BB-8 - F
Avoid the Police: B

31 Hidden Targets:
A. Boba Fett
B. Obi-wan Kenobi
C. Princess Leia
D. Chewbacca

Odd One Out: B

34-35 Lighsaber Repair:
A + H + J
B + E + K
D + G + I

Scrambled Names:
1. Mace Windu
2. Obi-Wan Kenobi
3. Luke Skywalker
4. Yoda

Force Shadows:
1. Chewbacca
2. R2-D2
3. C-3PO
4. Yoda

40-41 Missing Piece: 4
Which Exhaust Port: B

54-55 Play Sabacc!:
1. 6
2. A

56-57 Strips of a Ship:
A-4, B-1, C-3, D-2, E-10, F-6, G-9,
H-8, I-5, J-7

Ignition sequence:

Fix the ship: 2

59 Smuggler's Code:
1. Do not trust the Crimson Dawn
2. We are doing this my way
3. Just be charming

Hidden porgs found on pages: 6, 20, 33, 37, 44, 52, 62

22 Spot the Difference

24-25 The Secret Tunnels of Crait

30 Darth Vader Wordsearch

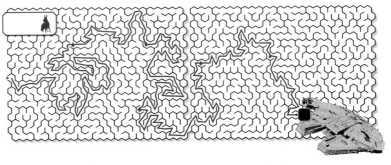

62-63 The Kessel Run

46-47 Where's the Wookiee?

66-67 Master of the Force: Quiz
1. Emperor Palpatine
2. Kyber
3. Darth Maul
4. Lando
5. Bounty Hunter
6. Podracing
7. Kylo Ren
8. Darth Vader
9. Praetorian Guards
10. Dagobah
11. Starkiller Base
12. Hux
13. W-wing
14. Wookiee
15. Purple
16. Ben Kenobi
17. Ahch-To
18. Astromech
19. FN-2187
20. Jakku